ON THE BRIGHT SIDE

Written by
Anastasia Difino

Illustrated by
Taylor Barron

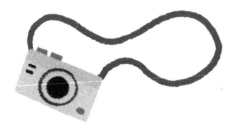

To my Frankie and Peter

On the bright side,
it's a beautiful day.

On the bright side,

school is only

a short walk away.

On the bright side, our flowers are blooming...
red, pink, purple, white.

COMMUNITY
GARDEN

So much beauty around me, life feels all right.

But sometimes,

the sad and the bad

do appear.

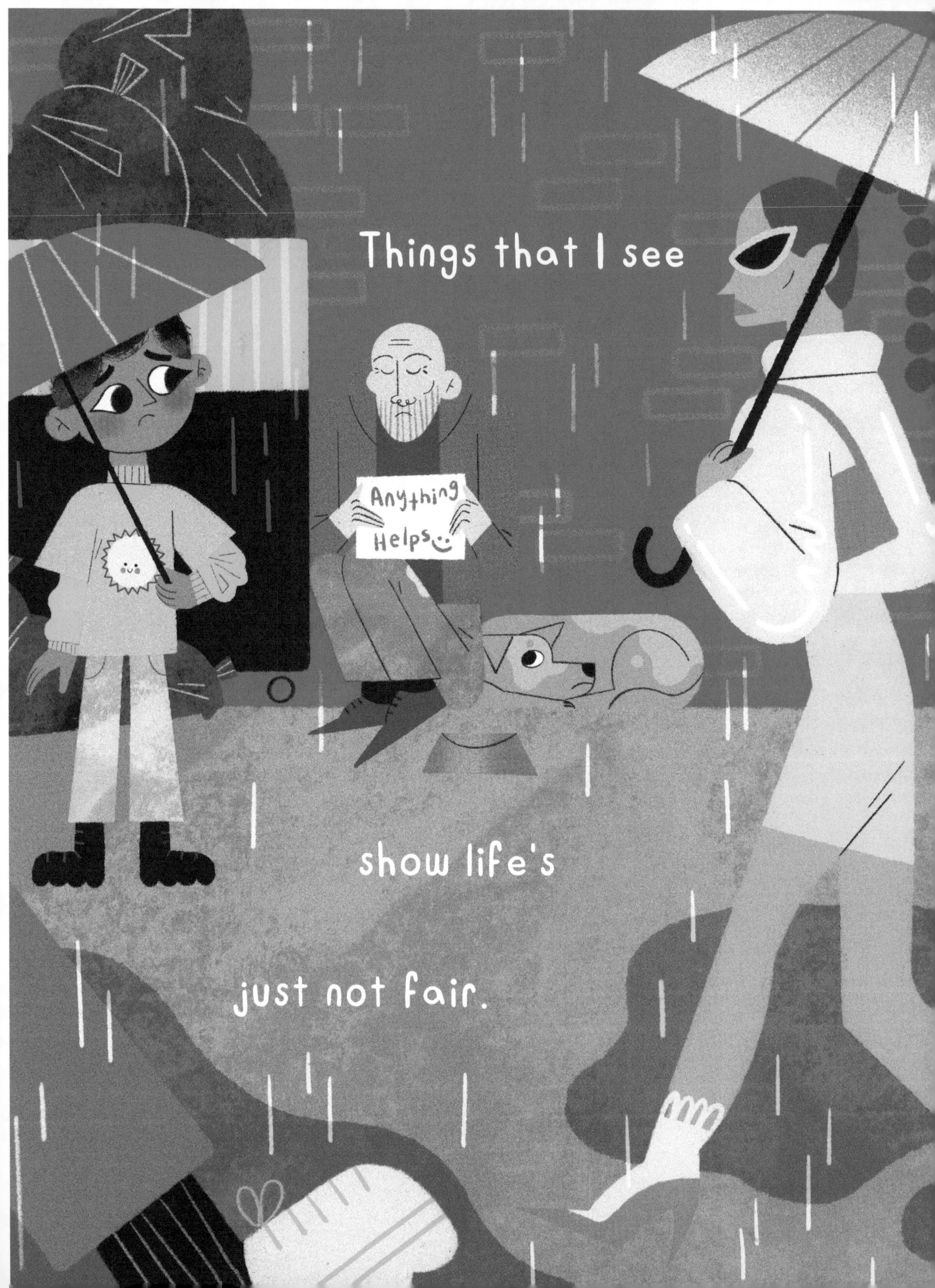

Things that I see

show life's

just not fair.

On the bright side, there's always someone who cares.

I care, but I'm small, I'm young, I'm just one.

The bright side's

a whole lot of ones

make a ton.

No way...I can't...

I don't stand a chance.

On the bright side,

we all speak art, music, and dance.

Our differences, at times,
may draw us apart.

On the bright side, however,
we all love with our heart.

Our love is connected
one way or another.

And the bright side of this

is we all have each other.

so difficult to face...

...but, on the bright side,

it can be a really,

really beautiful place.

Author's Note

The idea for this book, or rather a call of action, was born inside my very own classroom. I was inspired and challenged by my 5th graders to put something together with the hopes of instilling in them a positive mindset and brighter outlook in the beautiful things we have in life.

In the midst of our annual community projects, my students were becoming aware of issues around us - heartbreaking issues that reflected injustice, harm, and crime in our world. These discoveries raised feelings of sadness, anxiety, fear, and frustration. Witnessing my kids on this emotional rollercoaster tore me apart. What do you

do when all you want to show your kids is the beauty of life, but know the importance of also raising awareness to the unkind? The world is beautiful, but the world can be ugly. And as much as we tend to focus on the negative in our lives, we should do better in encouraging our children to see the good, share the good, and be the good on this Earth.

So, to all the children of the world, I leave you off with this: I hope this book encourages you to remain positive through all of life's challenges. I hope this book inspires you to smile and look up. I hope this book helps you realize that, although you may be just one, your positive energy and attitude can spread positively all over. Look, think, act, be on the bright side of things, today, tomorrow, and always.

Anastasia DiFino

is an elementary school teacher striving to inspire young children to find and be their best selves, not only academically, but socially and emotionally. Born and raised in Queens, New York, she obtained a B.A. in Communications from Hofstra University and an M.A. in Education from Queens College. Writing a children's book has been a long time dream of hers and, so, *On The Bright Side* was born with goals of promoting optimism and togetherness in children. When she's not in the classroom, Anastasia can be found loving life in New York with her husband and two boys.

Taylor Barron

Taylor Barron is an artist and award winning illustrator who has worked on over 10 children's book titles. Taylor has a passion for bright colors, geometric forms, and loves to focus on diversity, mental health, and environmentalism in her work. She was born in Seattle, USA and currently lives in Paris, France. She spends her time illustrating, working on murals, and painting.